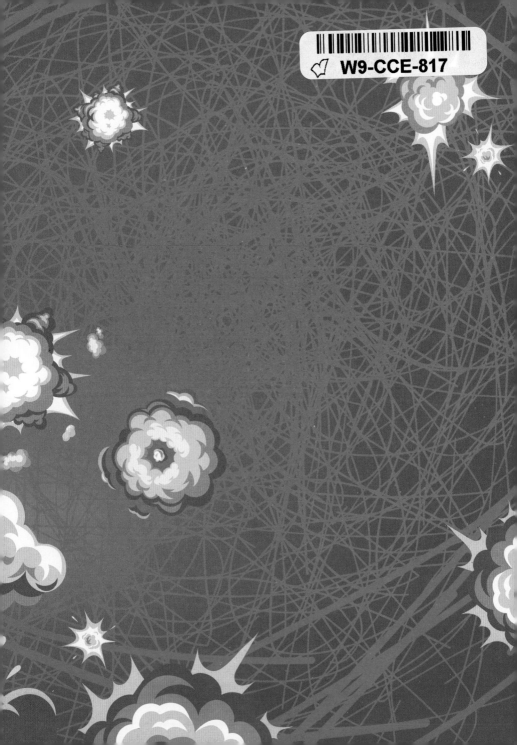

DUDE!
DO NOT OPEN
THIS BOOK!

CREATED BY
MICKEY & CHERYL GILL

Fine Print Publishing Company
PO Box 916401
Longwood, FL 32791-6401

Created in the USA & Printed in China
This book is printed on acid-free paper.

ISBN 978-1-892951-99-1

2 4 6 8 10 9 7 5 3 1

fprint.net

ALARMS ARE SOUNDING!
AN ALIEN INVASION IS HEADED
ZOMBIES ARE ROAMING THE EAR

RELEASE THE KRACKEN AND GET READY TO LAUNCH YOUR BRAIN INTO OVERDRIVE BECAUSE **DUDE, YOU OPENED THIS BOOK!**

PUT THE SPACE BETWEEN YOUR EARS TO THE ULTIMATE TEST. ROCKET TO MARS. CONSTRUCT AN ELECTRONIC POWER GLOVE. ANSWER CRAZY QUESTIONS. RATE THE FIVE BEST PIZZAS. SCARE YOUR BROS!

HEED THIS WARNING — EXPLOSIVE MIND MISSILES READY TO LAUNCH!!!

ROCKET PEN STANDS UP ON ITS OWN!

BRAIN

WHAT HAVE YOU HELD WITH YOUR BARE HANDS?

- ☒ BABY CHICK
- ☒ SNAKE
- ☒ FISH

Iphone 14

↑ FAVORITE ELECTRONIC DEVICE?

COULD YOU BE TRUSTED WITH GOVERNMENT SECRETS?

☒ YES ☐ ABSOLUTELY NOT

Top secret

WOULD YOU TAKE A ROCKET TO MARS?

☐ YES ☐ MAYBE ☒ NO WAY!

BODY BIO

HOW OLD ARE YOU?

HOW MANY INCHES ARE THERE BETWEEN YOUR EYES?

CAN YOU TOUCH YOUR NOSE WITH YOUR TONGUE?
☐ YES ☒ NO

ARE YOU OK IN TIGHT SPACES?
☐ YES
☐ I DON'T KNOW
☒ NO!

MILD ☒
MEDIUM ☐
HOT! ☐

WHICH WOULD YOU LIKE TO VISIT?

☐ ICELAND ☐ POLAND ☒ DISNEYLAND

BEST
SUPERHERO
MOVIE EVER?

A VenGERS

☒ RANCH DRESSING MAKES EVERYTHING TASTE
☐ KETCHUP
☐ CHEESE SAUCE **BETTER!**

HOW DO YOU LIKE YOUR WAFFLES?
☐ MAPLE SYRUP
☒ WHIPPED CREAM
☐ OTHER

WHAT MAKES YOU REALLY SLEEPY?

When I Goto school And DID Not skep Just night

THINK YOU COULD LIVE IN AN ?
☐ NOPE!
☒ YEP!

■ OUTER SPACE
☒ PLANET EARTH   ■ ANOTHER DIMENSION?

What is he destroying? Add it here →

SHOOT LASER BEAMS FROM EVIL CAT'S EYES

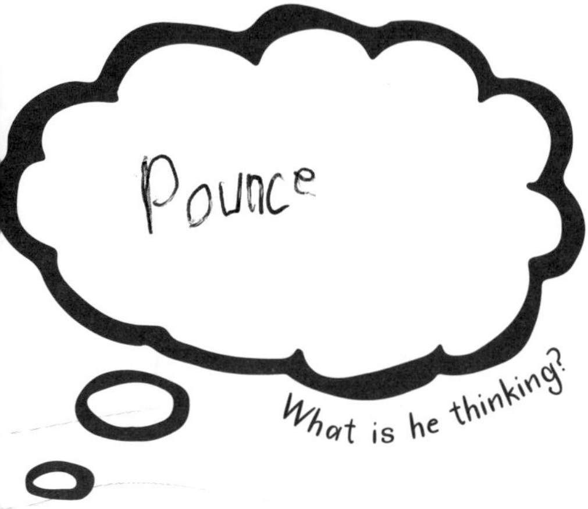

THESE ARE GERMS

Assign them a location
(in your ear, on a doorknob, and other places).
Then, give each one a name.

Location ⭕ Sneaker

Name

Location

Name

Location

Name

I feel sick.

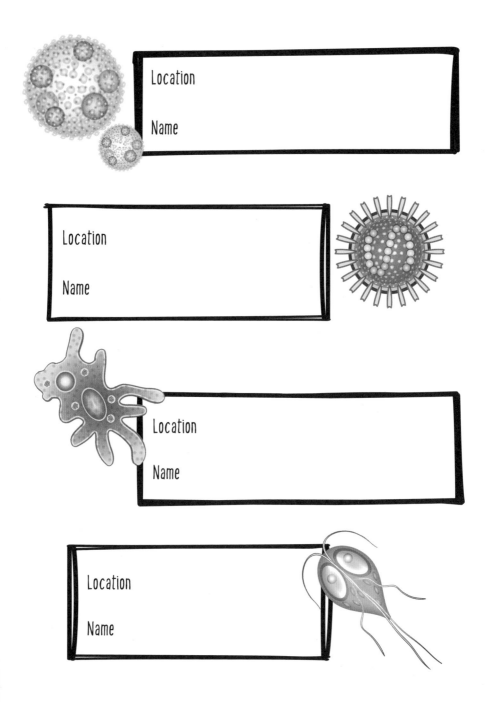

Location

Name

Location

Name

Location

Name

Location

Name

YOU DISCOVER YOU CAN FLY!

DO YOU TELL ANYONE? WHO?
OR, DO YOU KEEP IT A SECRET? HOW?

WHERE WILL
YOU FLY?

WHO WOULD WIN?

- ❏ VIKING ❏ PIRATE
- ❏ NINJA ❏ ROBOT
- ❏ YETI

- ❏ CORN DOG
- ❏ CORN ON THE COB
- ❏ POPCORN
- ❏ CANDY CORN?

WOULD YOU RATHER HAVE A TRAINED
- ❏ FALCON ❏ DOLPHIN ❏ SQUIRREL?

COOLEST CAR?

FAVORITE CRUMBS TO EAT?

DO YOU

☐ LICK YOUR FINGERS
☐ WIPE YOUR HANDS ON YOUR SHIRT
☐ USE A NAPKIN?

WHO'S THE ABSOLUTE WORST SUPERVILLAIN?

WHAT WOULD YOU CALL THIS?

WHAT DOES IT DO?

DRAW FACES ON THESE PICKLES
GIVE THEM EMOTIONS LIKE MAD, SAD AND HAPPY

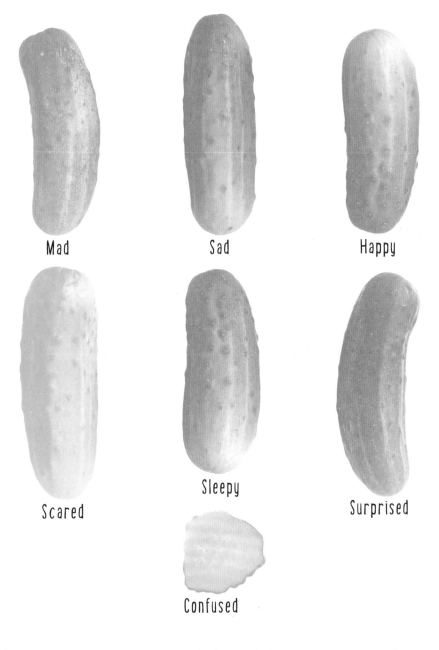

Mad

Sad

Happy

Scared

Sleepy

Surprised

Confused

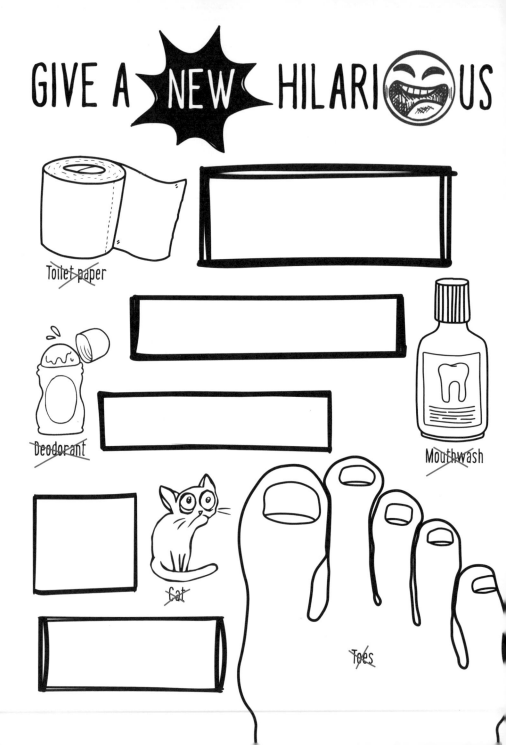

NAME TO EACH ONE OF THESE

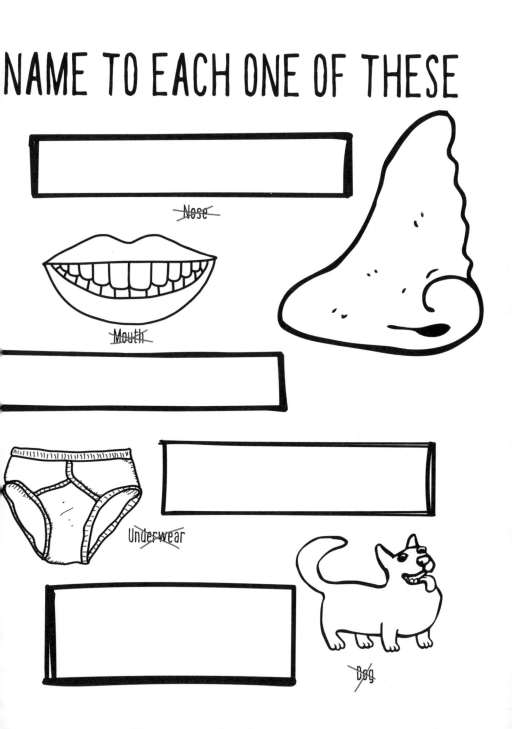

Nose

Mouth

Underwear

Dog

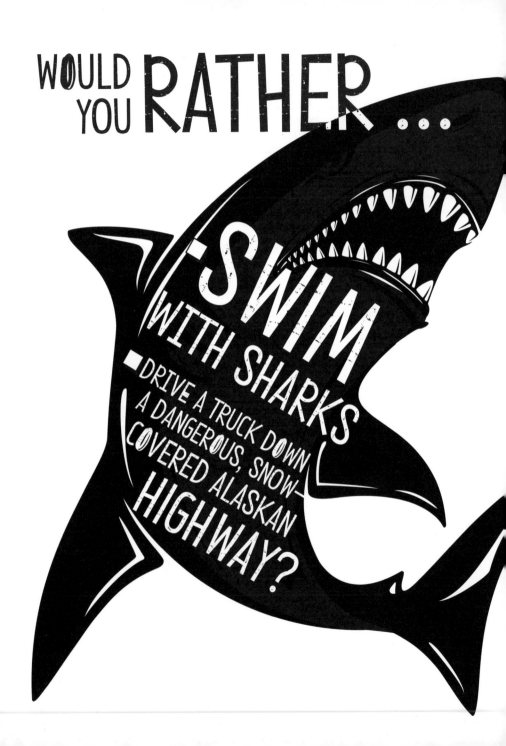

☐ EAT AN ENTIRE RAW ONION

☐ MUNCH ON A CAN OF DRIED WORMS?

HANG OUT WITH
A BUNCH OF

☐ MOVIE STARS ON A MOVIE SET

☐ STUNT MEN ON A MOVIE SET

☐ PEOPLE SETTING UP THE SNACK TABLE FOR MOVIE STARS AND STUNT MEN?

MOVE LIKE A(N)

☐ NINJA

☐ PRO FOOTBALL PLAYER

☐ OLYMPIC DOWNHILL SKIER?

☐ CLIMB THE **HIGHEST MOUNTAIN**

☐ RIDE THE TALLEST **ROLLER COASTER?**

GET A PIEC

1. DRAW A BUNCH OF DOTS ON THESE PAGES.
2. CONNECT THE DOTS.
3. GIVE YOUR CONSTELLATION A NAME.

E OF CHALK

constellation name

Nightmares are the worst!

What was your last one about? ➡

IF YOU FOUND A PIRATE'S TREASURE MAP, WOULD YOU

- THINK IT'S A JOKE
- GOOGLE IT TO SEE IF IT'S REAL
- PACK A BAG AND START SEARCHING?

WHAT'S THE COOLEST THING ABOUT A PIRATE?

- HOW HE TALKS
- HIS SWAGGER
- THE SHIP!

WOULD YOU RATHER HANG OUT
- IN THE CROW'S NEST
- ON THE POOP DECK?

- TALKING PARROT
- TRAINED MONKEY?

WOULD YOU RATHER HAVE A(N)
- EYE PATCH
- WOODEN LEG
- HOOK?

DRAW A DROID OF DOOM!

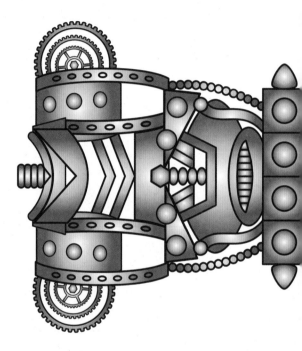

ADD

ALL

THE

MISSING

PARTS

TO

CREATE

YOUR

ROBOT

name of creation

BRR

His breath STINKS!

Draw or list what's
rotting in his stomach
↓

aPP

WHAT'S

THE WEIRDEST ANIMAL?

SCARIER?

- [ ] EXPLORING OUTER SPACE
- [ ] JOURNEYING TO THE BOTTOM OF THE SEA

CRAZY STUNT YOU'D LIKE TO TRY?

THE MOST HILARIOUS MOVIE?

MOST ANNOYING THING GIRLS DO?

FAVORITE THING TO DO BAREFOOT?

COOLER?

- ☐ SCUBA DIVING
- ☐ SKYDIVING

THE TASTIEST SAUCE EVER?

MAKE YOUR
OWN HELMET

Add horns, lights, or devices you need to protect yourself

DESIGN A COOL TEE

List the
5 BEST
pizza slices

1. _____
2. _____
3. _____
4. _____
5. _____

WHAT DO YOU GET IN SO MUCH TROUBLE FOR?

(AND, IT'S TOTALLY WORTH IT.)

THIS IS YOUR PERSONAL
SUPERHERO
GIVE HIM AN AMAZING COSTUME

WHAT OR WHO SHOULD HE DEFEND YOU AGAINST?

1. _____
2. _____
3. _____
4. _____
5. _____

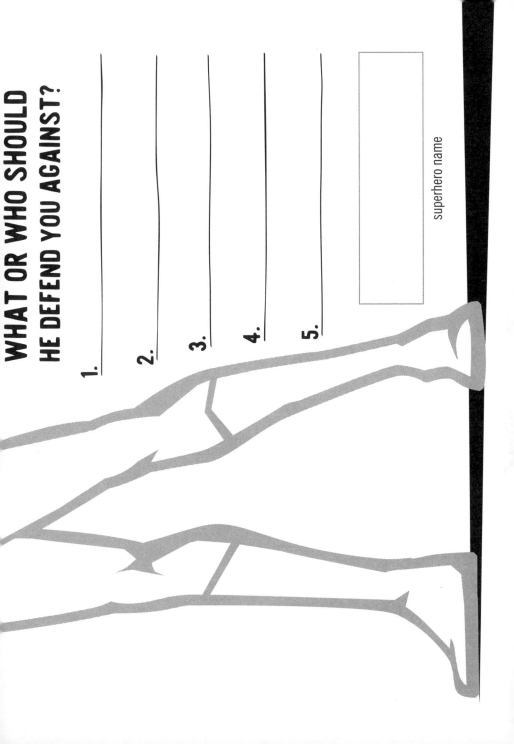

superhero name

SOMETHING YOU THINK IS TOTALLY DISGUST- ING?

WHAT DO YOU NEED A YEAR'S SUPPLY OF?

❑ FIRECRACKERS   ❑ CHICKEN TENDERS

❑ OTHER [   ]

[   ]

WOULD YOU RATHER

❑ WRESTLE AN ALLIGATOR
❑ RIDE A BUCKING BRONCO
❑ CATCH A SHARK?

❑ MEATBALL
❑ PAINTBALL
❑ SNOWBALL

PARTY?

AMAZING SPACECRAFT EVER!

THESE BOTTLES CONTAIN THE WORST SMELLS YOU KNOW

WHICH SCHOOL SUBJECT MAKES YOUR HEAD HURT?

WHAT OR WHO DO YOU NEED TO STAY AT LEAST 10 FEET AWAY FROM AT ALL TIMES?

CHOCOLATE-COVERED

- ❏ PEANUTS
- ❏ RAISINS
- ❏ PRETZELS
- ❏ ANTS
- ❏ _____ ?

WOULD YOU RATHER

- ❏ BREATHE UNDERWATER
- ❏ SCALE TALL BUILDINGS
- ❏ HAVE INCREDIBLE STRENGTH?

WHAT COULD YOU TOTALLY USE?

- ❏ ANOTHER EYE
- ❏ A TANK
- ❏ AN INVISIBILITY CLOAK

SOMETHING RIDICULOUS ADULTS MAKE YOU DO?

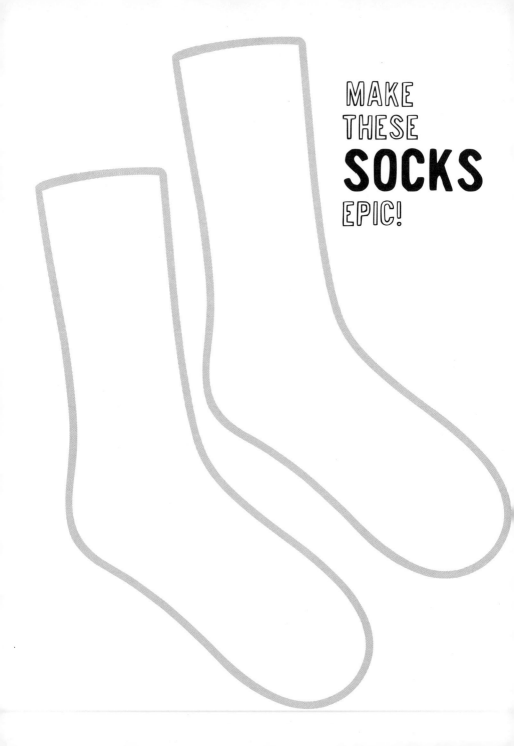

MAKE
THESE
SOCKS
EPIC!

NOW
ADD
SMELLY
FUMES
TO
THEM

THE INK BLOT TEST

There's no right or wrong answer!
What do you see? What do your friends see?

Log it here

Name	Describe what you see

WHICH DANGEROUS ANIMAL OR MAKE-BELIEVE CREATURE WOULD YOU LIKE AS A PET?

WHAT WOULD YOU CALL HIM?

FILL IN HIS ID TAG

WHAT KIND OF CRUNCHY FOOD WOULD HE EAT?

WRITE IT ON THE BAG

WHICH DO YOU THINK
REEKS THE WORST?

- ☐ HIPPO BREATH
- ☐ BABBOON FARTS
- ☐ YOUR BRO'S ARMPITS
- ☐ YOUR SOCKS

WHAT COULD YOU STAY UP ALL NIGHT FOR?

What stinks?

WHICH ONE OF YOUR FRIENDS WOULD BE AN AMAZING SPY?

WHY?

FINISH THIS SENTENCE

I WOULD LIKE TO BUILD THE PERFECT

☐ HOUSE
☐ CAR
☐ ROBOT
☐ BURRITO.

BRING THE BEAST TO LIFE!

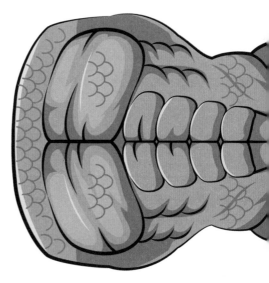

ADD
ALL
THE
MISSING
PARTS
TO
CREATE
YOUR
BEAST

name of creation

Keep track of what people say to you

1 _____

2 _____

3 _____

4 _____

5 _____

6 _____

7 _____

8 _____

9 _____

10 _____

FOOD YOU'D LIKE TO ROAST OVER A CAMPFIRE

1 _____

2 _____

3 _____

4 _____

5 _____

THINGS YOU'D LIKE TO THROW INTO A CAMPFIRE

1 _____

2 _____

3 _____

4 _____

5 _____

WHICH
ONE
OF
YOUR
BROS

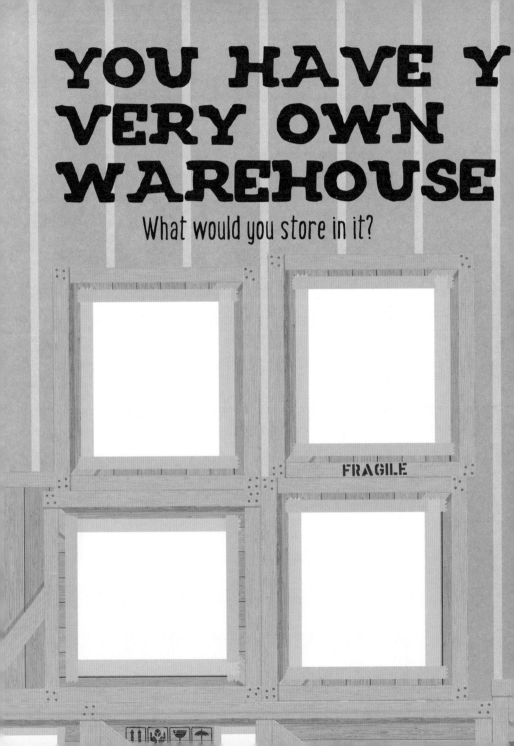

Label each crate with
what's inside
(lots of spicy beef jerky,
everything under your bed,
a motorcycle, etc.)

FRAGILE

FRAGILE

If you were
in charge
of dinner

what would
you eat each
night?

Sun. _____

Mon. _____

Tues. _____

Wed. _____

Thur. _____

Fri. _____

Sat. _____

NAME YOUR OWN PLANET

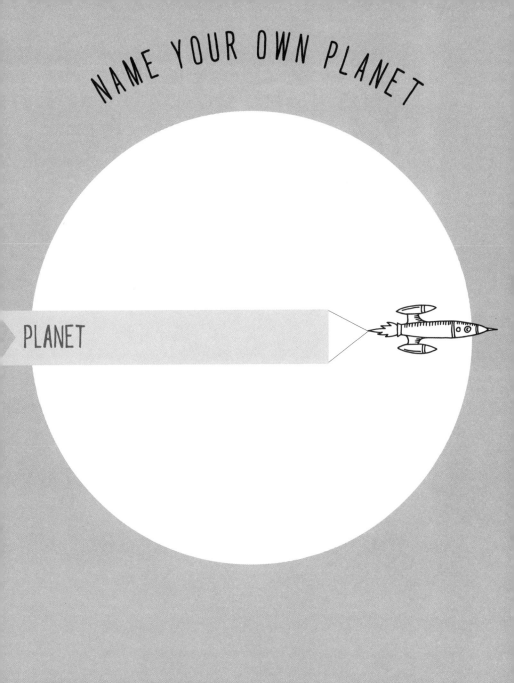

PLANET

Add land and water to it. Surround it with moons and other planets.

TRACE YOUR HAND HERE 👈

USE IT TO CREATE AN

ELECTRONIC POWER GLOVE!!!

ADD FINGER ROCKETS, LASER BEAMS, POWER BUTTONS, TOOLS, AND OTHER COOL GADGETS THAT YOU NEED

HERE IS A MOUTH

What or who does it belong to? Draw the rest.

TROPHY YOU'D LIKE TO WIN

BEST

EVER

Fill it in

YOU ARE
BEING SENT TO A
REMOTE
ISLAND
FOR A SECRET MISSION

1. WHO WILL YOU TAKE WITH YOU?

2. WHAT FOOD WILL YOU BRING?

3. OTHER THINGS YOU WILL PACK?

YOU'RE AMAZING!

DESIGN A FLAG FOR YOURSELF

ADD STRIPES, SYMBOLS, ANIMALS, OR WHATEVER YOU WANT

WHICH
IS
GROSSER?

❑ TOENAILS ❑ TONGUE

❑ RAW OYSTERS ❑ ANCHOVIES

❑ DOG BREATH ❑ CAT FOOD

❑ ROACHES ❑ RATS

❑ PIMPLE ❑ COLD SORE

❑ SCABS ❑ BOOGERS

❑ YOUR BATHROOM ❑ YOUR BEDROOM

❑ COOKED CABBAGE ❑ STINKY CHEESE

❑ COW PATTY ❑ MOLDY HAMBURGER PATTY

❑ SPINACH ❑ KALE

TAPE SOMETHING INTO EACH SPACE OF THIS DRAWER. COINS, LEAVES, NOTES, ETC.

TEAR THIS PAGE OUT OF BOOK. TAKE IT

EVERYWHERE WITH YOU FOR ONE WEEK. PUT IT IN YOUR BACKPACK. PLACE YOUR DRINKS ON IT. TAKE NOTES ON IT. SHOVE IT IN YOUR POCKET. TAPE IT BACK IN THE BOOK.

TEAR THIS PAGE OUT OF BOOK. TAKE IT EVERYWHERE WITH YOU FOR ONE WEEK. PUT IT IN YOUR BACKPACK. PLACE YOUR DRINKS ON IT. TAKE NOTES ON IT. SHOVE IT IN YOUR POCKET. TAPE IT BACK IN THE BOOK.

Fill in this mask and cut it out. Cut out eyes and mouth holes. Poke holes in the sides and thread string through them. Put on mask and scare your friends.

This mask is reversible! Fill in this side too.

Fill in this message. Cut it out. Fold it up so OPEN THIS SECRET MESSAGE is showing. Leave it somewhere for someone you know to find.

IF YOU FIND THIS SECRET MESSAGE, HIDE IT

_____
Location

ON _____.
Date

LEAVE A SECRET MESSAGE FOR ME WITH IT.

Fold up message along the dotted lines so
OPEN THIS SECRET MESSAGE is showing.

OPEN THIS SECRET MESSAGE	OPEN THIS SECRET MESSAGE	OPEN THIS SECRET MESSAGE
OPEN THIS SECRET MESSAGE	OPEN THIS SECRET MESSAGE	OPEN THIS SECRET MESSAGE
OPEN THIS SECRET MESSAGE	OPEN THIS SECRET MESSAGE	OPEN THIS SECRET MESSAGE

DESTROY THIS PAGE!
DRAW ALL OVER IT. PUNCH HOLES IN IT.
SCRATCH IT. STAPLE IT. CUT IT UP WITH SCISSORS.
TAPE IT BACK TOGETHER.

DESTROY THIS PAGE!

DRAW ALL OVER IT. PUNCH HOLES IN IT.
SCRATCH IT. STAPLE IT. CUT IT UP WITH SCISSORS.
TAPE IT BACK TOGETHER.

WARNING

Fill in sign with a hilarious warning. Hang on bedroom or bathroom door.

CAUTION

IN PROGRESS

Fill in sign with a ridiculous caution. Hang on bedroom or bathroom door.

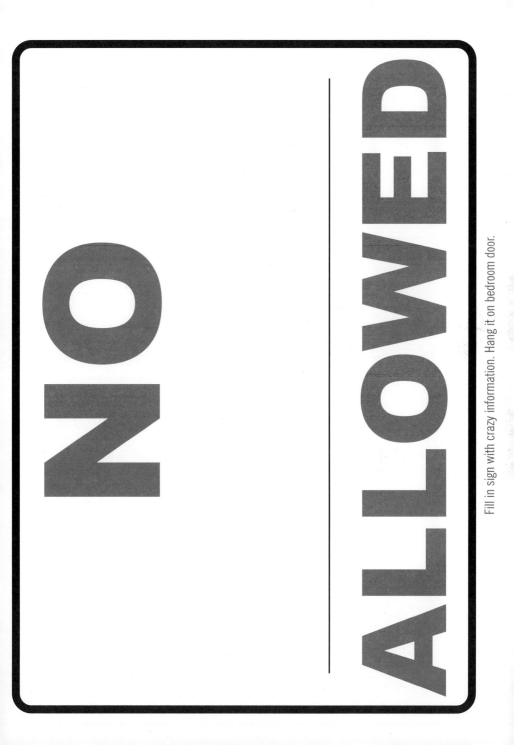

NO ALLOWED

Fill in sign with crazy information. Hang it on bedroom door.

CAUTION

WORKING ABOVE

_____

Fill in sign with crazy caution. Hang on door, wall, or window.

BEWARE OF

Fill in sign with ridiculous warning. Hang on bedroom or bathroom door.

SECURITY NOTICE

THIS AREA IS PROTECTED BY

TRESPASSERS WILL BE

Fill in sign with funny information. Hang it on bedroom door.

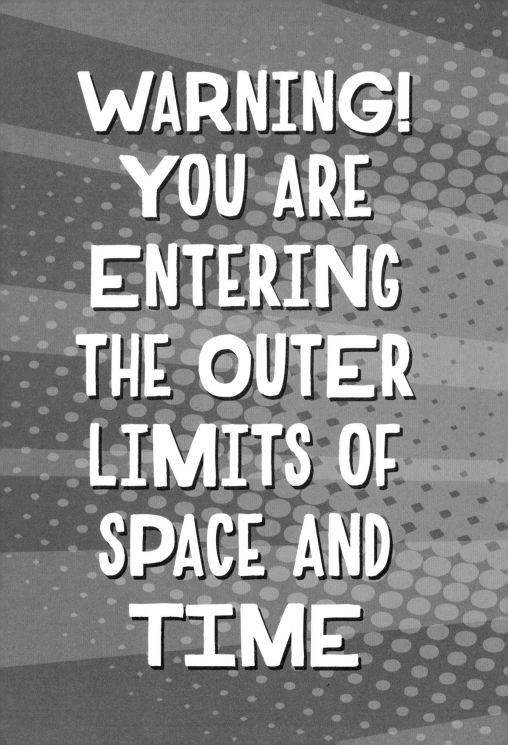